A BEVERIDGE

Contents

Answers to the questions are on the back of the Pull-out Poster in the centre of the book.

Published by Coordination Group Publications Ltd.

Contributors:
Angela Billington
Charley Darbishire
Chris Dennett
Katherine Stewart
Tim Wakeling
James Paul Wallis

ISBN 1 84146 262 4
Groovy website: www.cgpbooks.co.uk
Jolly bits of clipart from CorelDRAW
Printed by Elanders Hindson, Newcastle upon Tyne.

Feeling How Warm Things Are

You can't tell how hot things are by just looking or smelling — you have to feel them.
But be careful — <u>never</u> touch anything that might be really hot or you might burn yourself.

Q1 Put a circle around the best way of
telling whether your bath is hot or cold.

By Listening.

By Smelling.

By Touching.

By Looking.

Q2 My mate Kevin reckons he can tell whether one thing is hotter than another by touching them.
I reckon if two things are nearly the same temperature he won't be able to tell the <u>difference</u>.
Put a tick in the box next to the pairs of things you think Kevin <u>could</u> judge temperatures for.

and...

A Cup of Tea   **A Cup of Coffee**

 and...

Igloo   **Electric Blanket (switched on)**

and...

Cat   **Dog**

 and...

Ice cream   **Freshly Baked Pizza**

Q3 Fill in the missing words in this bit of writing using the words in the boxes.

You can feel the .... of different things.

But .... things .... the best way to find their

temperature. It .... more accurate to use a ....

| thermometer | is not |

| temperature |

| touching |

| is |

Do this page — or you'll be in hot water...

It's not as easy as it looks — it's quite hard to feel the difference in temperature between things.
One thing has to be a fair bit hotter than the other before you can feel the difference.

Thermometers

Thermometers are really ace — they tell you exactly what the temperature of something is.

You measure temperature in degrees Celsius. When temperature is written down, degrees Celsius is shortened to °C. The liquid inside the thermometer moves up and down the scale to show the temperature.

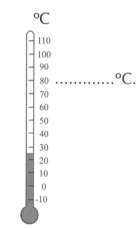

EXAMPLE
°C

This thermometer is showing 60°C.

Don't hold the bulb of the thermometer when you're trying to read it — the heat from your hand will make the reading wrong.

Bulb

Ace Thermometer pens — write and measure temperature at the same time.

Q1 Look at the example above of how to read a thermometer the right way. Write the temperatures next to the other thermometers.

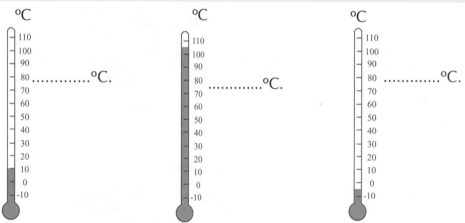

°C ....°C.   °C ....°C.   °C ....°C.   °C ....°C.

Q2 Shade in the following thermometers so that they show the temperatures written next to them.

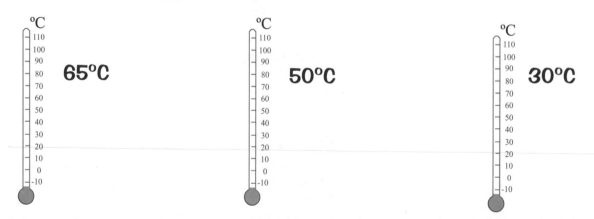

65°C   **50°C**   **30°C**

Don't tell me this page is too hot to handle...

Thermometers are great. With one of these little beauties, you don't need to try to guess how hot something is by feeling it. You can actually measure it. You need to know how to read one, mind...

Temperature Around Things

The temperature <u>around</u> something affects how hot that thing will be — like when it's snowing in winter you feel cold and have to wear more clothes, or sit by a fire. If you leave something in one place for several hours, it will have the <u>same temperature</u> as its surroundings.

Q1 a) Fill in the right temperature a bowl of <u>hot</u> water will have after it's been left for 10 hours in a room at 20°C — choose from the numbers in the box. Then shade in the right temperature on the thermometer.

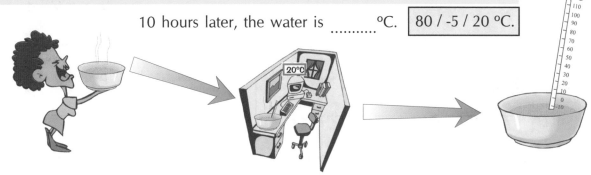

10 hours later, the water is .... °C.   80 / -5 / 20 °C.

b) If you put a bowl of <u>cold</u> water in the same room for 10 hours, its temperature will be .... °C.

Q2 Here are some more objects left in a room with a temperature of 20°C. For each one, use one of the numbers in the boxes to fill in their temperatures after 10 hours.

After 10 hours in a room with a temperature of 20°C...

...a cup of tea would have a temperature of .... °C

20 / 87 / 5

...a packet of frozen peas would have a temperature of .... °C

-15 / 0 / 20

...a cake from the oven would have a temperature of .... °C

180 / 20 / 65

Q3 Write UP or DOWN next to each of these sentences, to show what happens to the thermometer when you do these things to it.

The temperature shown goes **DOWN**.
The temperature shown goes **UP**.

Hold the thermometer under cold running water. ....

Hold the thermometer next to a light bulb. ....

Hold the thermometer on a radiator or heater. ....

Room temperature — yes there's room for a temperature...

The things in a room will end up the same temperature as the room — even if it takes them a while.

Temperatures at Different Times

A room gets colder at night, warmer in the day, and even hotter if the heating's on.

Q1   The temperature in the classroom changes during the day as different things happen. Draw a line between the temperature and what is happening in the classroom. I've put the time next to the temperature.

Mrs Noseybonce always got hot under the collar.

12:00 midnight	5°C
9:00 in the morning	18°C
10:00 in the morning	23°C
2:30 in the afternoon	16°C

The teacher has opened the window.
It's the middle of the night.
The teacher has turned the heater on.
The children come into the classroom.

Q2   All the pictures below show things with different temperatures.
Write a letter under each thermometer to match them with the right pictures.

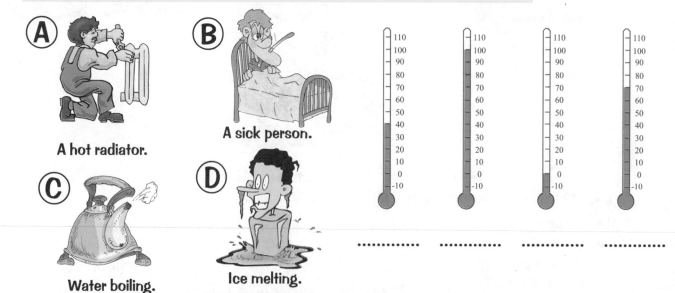

A hot radiator.

A sick person.

Water boiling.

Ice melting.

Temperature changes — in the changing rooms...

Phew — that's a lot of numbers. You don't have to learn them all. If you know that 0° is freezing and that body temperature is higher than room temperature, you're doing great.

Temperatures in Different Places

You may have noticed that different rooms and places in your house are different temperatures.

Q1   For each picture of a place, write whether you think it is hotter or colder than normal (normal means in the middle of your lounge on a normal day).

Write either "warmer" or "colder" underneath the pictures.

In an unheated cellar.

....

Next to an oven (switched on).

....

Behind a door (draughty).

....

In a greenhouse
(on a sunny summer day).

....

On a windowsill
(on a snowy day).

....

The freezer was at Henry's favourite temperature.

In front of an open fire.

....

Dark cellars — they send shivers down my spine...

Easy stuff, this. Just work out whether that place would feel warm or cold.

Temperatures at Different Times

Graphs can be used to show how temperature changes as time goes by.
They make it obvious when something has made the temperature hotter or colder.

Q1   Match the points of the graph with the events that happened
through the day to change the temperature in the room.

Write the letters in
these boxes.

Everyone leaves and the teacher turns the heating off.

Mildred lets some fresh air into the room by
throwing a rugby ball through the window.

The teacher arrives and turns the heating on in the classroom.

The room cools down to the temperature outside.

Mr Smogweed the caretaker patches the hole in the window.

It's a bit chilly here Mrs Kettlebottom...

Leo suddenly found a
rugby ball where Q.4
should have been.

OK, I did it, but don't graph me up...

If this graph looks a bit tricky, don't panic — just remember that the line goes up when it gets
warmer, down when it gets colder, and is level when it stays the same. Makes sense, really.

Cooling Down

The place something is in affects its temperature. A polar bear will be colder than a koala, and a penguin's likely to be chillier than a flamingo. The same is true for things that aren't alive as well.

Q1 Look at these graphs showing how a bowl of hot water, with a temperature of 80°C, cools down over 60 minutes in different places. The titles for three of the graphs are in the box below — write them above the correct graphs. On the blank graph draw how the hot water would cool if left in a freezer with a temperature of -20°C.

Hot Water (80°C) Left in a Room (20°C)   Hot Water (80°C) Left next to a Heater (60°C)

Hot Water (80°C) Left in a Fridge (3°C)

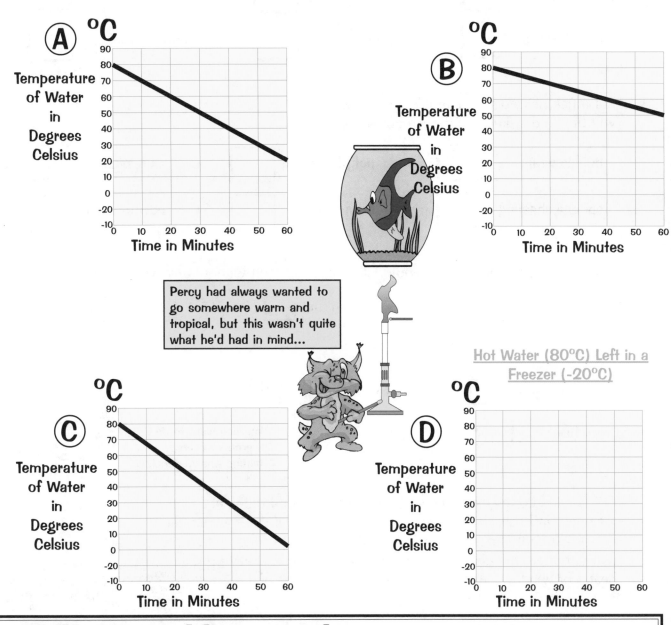

Percy had always wanted to go somewhere warm and tropical, but this wasn't quite what he'd had in mind...

Hot Water (80°C) Left in a Freezer (-20°C)

Chill out and keep cool...

Basically, the colder the surroundings, the faster the temperature will go down. That makes sense — if you're out in the snow, you get cold pretty quick. It's all common sense, really.

8

Keeping Things Cold

PROJECT ONE — Find out what's best at keeping ice frozen.

Try to find out what would be a good material for Penelope to use to keep her ice cream frozen by covering ice cubes in different materials and seeing how long it takes the ice to melt.

More ice cream please!

Penelope quite liked ice cream.

Q1　Do this experiment if you can. Here's a list of materials — choose four to test and put a tick ✔ next to the ones you've chosen.

bubble wrap ☐　　polythene bag ☐　　aluminium foil ☐

sponge sheeting ☐　　newspaper ☐　　cotton wool ☐

Q2　Put a tick next to the materials you think will be good at keeping the ice cold.

bubble wrap ☐　　polythene bag ☐　　aluminium foil ☐

sponge sheeting ☐　　newspaper ☐　　cotton wool ☐

Q3　a) How long do you think it would take for ice to melt without any wrapping?

2 minutes ☐　　1 hour ☐　　6 days ☐

b) How often should you check the ice?

Every 30 seconds ☐　　Every 15 minutes ☐

Every hour ☐

You may want to do it in groups, each group testing one material.

What do you mean how long before the ice melts?

Q4　OK, go and do the experiment. Wrap ice cubes in 4 different materials and check them every 15 minutes to see if they have melted or are still partly frozen. Remember to be careful to keep all the ice cubes in the same place while you're testing them — away from a heater or window. And don't forget to makes notes of the results.

Sometimes you really don't want the ice to melt.

Is the freezer an insulator — it keeps it cold...

Wow, this is actually useful. Think of when you go on a picnic, and want to keep the drinks cold. After you've done this experiment you'll know what to wrap them in so they don't warm up.

Keeping Things Cold

When you've done an experiment, you should always write down your results.

Q1 Fill in this table by writing the names of the materials at the top and writing "melted" in the box at the time when the ice has melted. Put "not melted" in the boxes above it. I've filled in one material for you.

Time in hours	Material				
	My jumper				
½	Not melted				
1	Not melted				
1½	Melted				
2					
2½					
3					

Q2

a) In this table, just write the materials and the time it took the ice to melt.

Material				
Time in hours				

b) A bar chart is another way to show your results. Fill this one in. If you get stuck, have a look at the one on page 13.

\\\\ | | ||||| | | ||||/
Don't worry if you can't do the experiment — use these spare results:
/ / | | || | \|||||||| | ||\\

Spare Results:
Foil — ½ hour
Bubble wrap — 3 hours
Newspaper — 1½ hours
Cotton wool — 2 hours

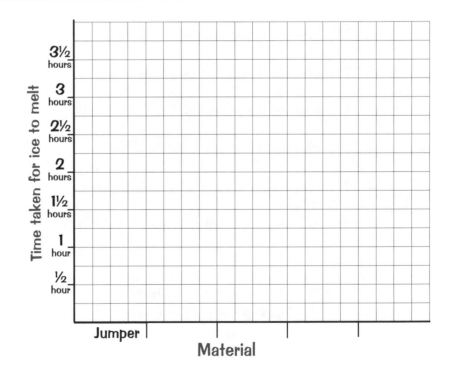

A shy ice cube — it melts into the background...

I hope you're actually doing this experiment — it's loads more fun than just using the spare results. By now, you should have a pretty good idea what'll be good at stopping the ice from melting.

Keeping Things Cold

Some of the materials on page 9 were better than others at keeping things cold.
It's worth knowing some of the reasons why they were.

Q1   Which material was the best insulator? Fill in the gaps with your results from the experiment or with our spare results.

An <u>insulator</u> is something that's good at keeping things hot or cold.

a)   .... was the best insulator.

It took .... minutes for the ice to melt.

b)   .... was the worst insulator.

It took .... minutes for the ice to melt.

c)   The difference between these times is .... minutes.

Next time we meet, we'll be water.

Let's hope I still recognise you.

Ice cubes starting to melt.

Q2   More than one material was a good insulator.
What did the good insulators have in common?
Put a tick ✔ next to the sentences that are correct, and a cross ✗ next to the incorrect ones.

a)   The best insulators are not made of metal.

b)   The best insulators are thicker than the others.

c)   The best insulators are all the same colour.

d)   The best insulators are dull, not shiny.

e)   The best insulators are all the same shape.

f)   The best insulators are light, not heavy.

g)   The best insulators are all the same size.

h)   The best insulators all like the same music.

I knew I should have brought my polystyrene vest...

Remember that you're keeping the <u>heat out</u>, not keeping the <u>cold in</u>.

How do you stop a snowman from melting?

Melting snowmen — snow joke...

Don't make the mistake of thinking this is all made up to give you stuff to do at school.
Finding what materials keep heat in is mega-important to companies who make clothes.

11

Keeping Things Cold

Q1　Here's a list of other containers and materials. Write "good" next to the ones you think would be good at keeping things cold, and "bad" next to the ones that would be bad at keeping things cold.

tin can ....　　　　　　　coolbox ....

plastic cup ....　　　sponge ....　　　bin-bag ....

thin tracing paper ....　　　metal saucepan ....

Q2　Is it better to use <u>two</u> layers of material or <u>one</u> thick layer? Try another experiment. Wrap ice cubes in insulating materials as you did before, and test how long it takes for the ice to melt. Use the two materials which were the best insulators. For both materials, test one thick layer and two thinner layers. Put "not melted" and "melted" in the boxes as you did on p.9.

1st material　　　　2nd material

Time in hours	One thick layer		Two normal layers	
½				
1½				
2				
2½				
3				

Which was best? .... (TWO LAYERS / ONE LAYER).

Q3　Fill in the gaps in the sentences by choosing from the words in brackets.

This is a nice easy one to finish with.

.... is trapped between the two layers.　　　(AIR / WATER)

Air is a good .... 　　　(INSULATOR / HEATER)

So having air between the layers will help keep the ice .... 　　(COOL / HOT).

A pair of hens — two layers...

OK, so you've done these four pages about keeping things cold. Now you should have a pretty good idea about what things will be good at keeping things cold. It's useful stuff, alright.

Keeping Things Warm

PROJECT TWO — Finding out which materials are good at keeping rice warm.

Do an experiment to find out what material is good at keeping food warm. Get some hot cooked rice, put it into piles and cover the piles in different materials. Leave the end of a thermometer in each pile and check the temperature of each pile every 15 minutes.

Q1   Here's a list of materials you could use to either put the rice in or wrap it up in — pick 4 to test and tick the ones you've chosen.

a) newspaper ☐   b) polystyrene box ☐   c) china bowl with lid ☐

d) saucepan with lid ☐   e) clingfilm ☐

Q2   Put a tick next to the materials below you think are good at keeping the rice warm. Put a cross next to the ones you think won't keep it warm long.

a) newspaper ....   b) polystyrene box ....

c) china bowl ....   d) saucepan ....

e) cling film ....

Make sure you put the rice piles in the same place — don't put one by the window and one under a lamp.

WARNING — be careful with anything hot. Make sure you don't burn yourself.

Q3   Fill in the gaps in this sentence about how long it might take rice to cool down without wrapping. Choose from the words below.

If I checked the temperature after .... , it wouldn't have cooled yet. It

might have cooled to room temperature after .... If I didn't check it until

after .... , it would have cooled ages ago. Leaving it for

.... would be just plain silly.

6 hours	several days
5 minutes	1 hour

Can't catch me!

Angus and Kim missed the last bus home with their takeaway.

Phew — this is hot stuff...

You can cheat, if you want. Well, it's not really cheating. You can think about what people actually use to keep things hot. I've seen people use polystyrene cups for keeping coffee hot in...

KS2 Science Answers — Keeping Warm

Q2:

Material	Newspaper	Foil	Polythene bag	Polystyrene
Time in minutes	45	15	30	60

Q3:

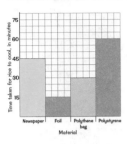

Page 14 Keeping Things Warm

Q1: Spare results = polystyrene

60

Foil

15

45

Q2: a) Quite thick   b) Light   c) Not metals

Q3: metals hot cold heavy colour

Page 15 Keeping Things Warm

Q1: a) ✘ b) ✔ c) ✘ d) ✘ e) ✔ f) ✘

Q2: **polystyrene box**, **china bowl with lid** would be good insulators

newspaper, **aluminium foil**, **saucepan with lid**, **clingfilm** would be bad insulators

Q3: thin layers

one layer

air   insulator

between

thin   layer

Page 16 Good Insulators

Q1: best at keeping things hot = polythene bag, polystyrene, jumper, towel

best at keeping things cold = bubble wrap, cotton wool, coolbox, sponge

Q2: are

are

Page 17 Good Insulators

Q1: good = polystyrene, thick foam sheeting, bubble wrap,

bad = cling film, a sheet of tissue paper, thin cotton

Q2: woollen blankets

Q3: insulator   material

good

hot   wool

Page 18 Metal, Plastic and Wood

Q1: Handles   wood   insulators   heat

metal   conductors

Q2: tin can = metal, knife blade = metal, plank = wood

see-through pen = plastic

Page 19 Metal, Plastic and Wood

Q1: She should not use the copper metal handle because it will get hot and burn her hand.

Q2: Copper metal because it needs to get heat through to heat the ingredients in the cauldron.

Q3: a) metal   b) heat-proof plastic or wood

Page 20 Electical and Heat Conductors

Q1: GOOD heat conductors = copper wire, brass pins, steel

BAD heat conductors = cable cover (plastic), plug cover (plastic), wood

Q2: GOOD electrical conductors = pan bottom (metal), zinc (metal), iron's bottom (metal)

BAD electrical conductors = pan handle (plastic), wooden mat, nylon (plastic), iron's handle (plastic)

Page 21 Everyday Insulators

Q1: a) Double glazed window b) Foam sheeting c) Winter jacket

d) Vacuum flask   e) Thick casserole dish

Q2: a) Cotton sunhat   b) Picnic box   c) Vacuum flask

d) Thick stone wall

Page 22 Keeping Things Cold

Q1: a) Foam sheeting b) Cloth c) Because it is a metal and therefore a bad insulator. It's also very thin.

Q2: A thermometer

Q3: Foam sheeting

Page 23 Keeping Things Hot or Cold

Q1: Wrap in polystyrene; put in a vacuum flask; put in the oven.

Q2: Wrap in bubble wrap; put in the freezer; wrap in foam sheeting

(any sensible answer)

Page 24 Revision Questions

Q1:

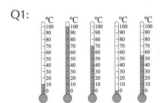

Q2: 5°C

Q3: Good: **bubble wrap** and **cotton wool** Bad: **foil** and **newspaper**

Q4: Yes

Q5:

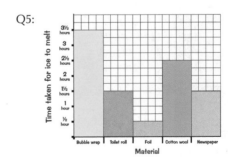

Page 25 Revision Questions

Q1: good   bad   good   good

plastic   wood   metal

Q2: TRUE

TRUE

Q3: copper wire   metal mug

Q4: 1) Wrap it in foam

2) Wrap it in bubble wrap

3) Sit on it (gently)

(any other sensible answer)

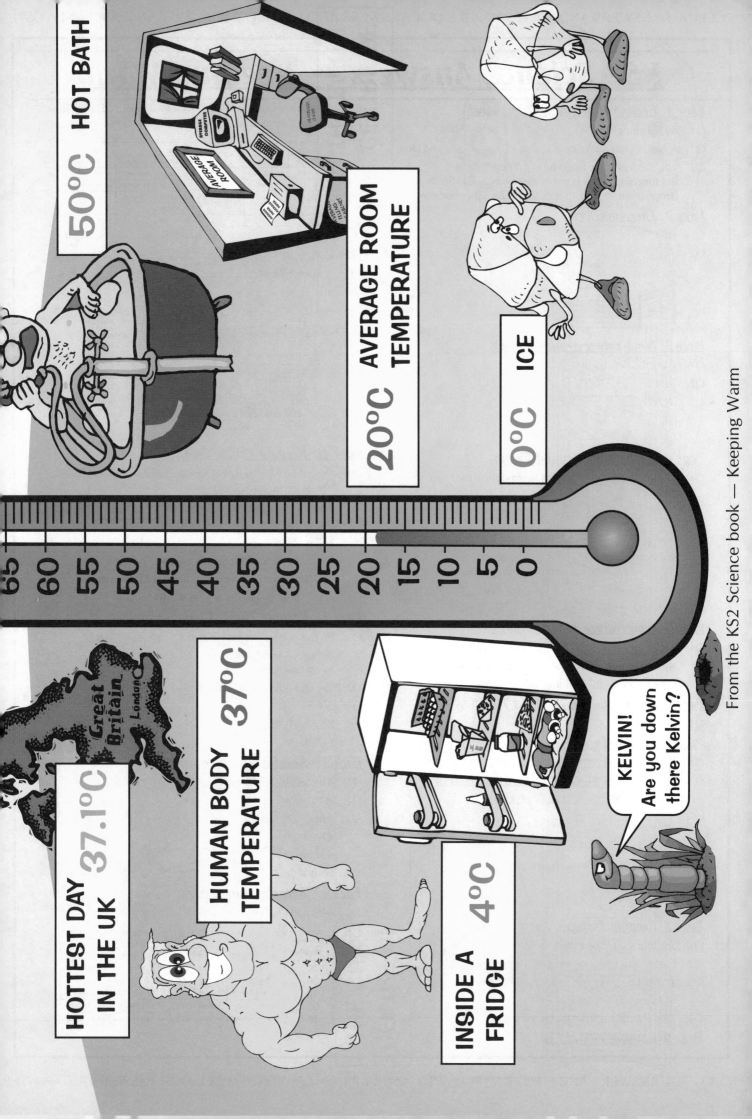

From the KS2 Science book — Keeping Warm

KS2 Science Answers — Keeping Warm

Page 1 Feeling How Warm Things Are

Q1: By Touching

Q2: A cup of Tea and A cup of coffee   Cat and Dog

Q3: You can feel the **temperature** of different things.
But **touching** things **is not** the best way to find their
temperature. It **is** more accurate to use a **thermometer**.

Page 2 Thermometers

Q1: 10°C   105°C   5°C   25°C

Q2:

Page 3 Temperature Around Things

Q1: a) 20°C   b) 20°C

Q2: 20°C   20°C   20°C

Q3: DOWN

UP

UP

Page 4 Temperature Around Things

Q1: 12:00   5°C _____   It's the middle of the night
midnight

  9:00   18°C _____   children come into the classroom
in the morning

  10:00   23°C _____   the teacher has turned the
in the morning   heater on.

  2:30   16°C _____   the teach has opened the
in the afternoon   window

Q2: B   C   D   A

Page 5 Temperature Around Things

Q1: Cellar = colder   Behind a door = colder

Next to an oven = warmer   In a green house = warmer

On a windowsill = colder   Open fire = warmer

Page 6 Temperature at Different Times

Q1: D   B   A   E   C

Page 7 Cooling Down

Q1: A = Hot Water (80ºC) Left in a Room (20ºC)

   B = Hot Water (80ºC) Left next to a Heater (60ºC)

   C = Hot Water (80ºC) Left in a Fridge (3ºC)

°C

Page 8 Keeping Things Cool

Q1: any four should be ticked

Q2: bubble wrap, sponge sheeting, cotton wool

Q3: a) 1 hour

b) Every 15 minutes

Q4: They should carry out the experiment.

Page 9 Keeping Things Cool

Q1: The table should be filled in with their results. Should look
like this if the "spare results" are used.

Time in hours	Material				
	My jumper	Foil	Bubble Wrap	Newspaper	Cotten Wool
½	Not melted	Melted	Not melted	Not melted	Not melted
1	Not melted		Not melted	Not melted	Not melted
1½	Melted		Not melted	Melted	Not melted
2			Not melted		Melted
2½			Not melted		
3			Melted		

Q2: a)

Material	Foil	Bubble Wrap	Newspaper	Cotton Wool
Time in hours	½	3	1½	2

b)

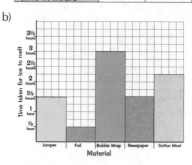

Page 10 Keeping Things Cool

Q1: Should be filled in with their own results. The answers
below are for the spare results.

a) **Bubble wrap** was the best insulator.

It took **180** minutes for the ice to melt.

b) **Foil** was the worst insulator.

It took **30** minutes for the ice to melt.

c) The difference between these times is **150** minutes.

Q2: a) ✔ b) ✔ c) ✗ d) ✔ e) ✗ f) ✔ g) ✗ h) ✗

Page 11 Keeping Things Cool

Q1: tin can = bad, coolbox = good, plastic cup = bad,
sponge = good, bin-bag = bad, thin tracing paper = bad,
metal saucepan = bad

Q2: The table should be completed with their results.

Q3: AIR

INSULATOR

COOL

Page 12 Keeping Things Warm

Q1: 4 materials should be ticked

Q2: a) ✗ b) ✔ c) ✔ d) ✗ e) ✗

Q3: 5 min

1 hour

6 hours

Several days

Page 13 Keeping Things Warm

The tables and graph below show the spare results.

Q1:

Time in minutes	Material			
	Newspaper	Foil	Polythene bag	Polystyrene
15	Hotter	Room temp.	Hotter	Hotter
30	Hotter	Room temp.	Room temp.	Hotter
45	Room temp.	Room temp.	Room temp.	Hotter
60	Room temp.	Room temp.	Room temp.	Room temp.
75	Room temp.	Room temp.	Room temp.	Room temp.

Keeping Things Warm

Timing how long it takes for the rice to get to exactly room temperature might take a very long time, so when it's <u>nearly</u> room temperature (5°C away), you can stop. Put another thermometer in the room (not too near a window or heater) so you know what room temperature is. Don't panic if you can't do the experiment — use the spare results from the bottom of the page.

Q1 Do the experiment and put your results in this table. I've done the first one for you, so you just need to do three more the same way or use the spare results in the bottom right corner.

Time in minutes	Material			
	Newspaper			
15	hotter			
30	hotter			
45	room temp.			
60	room temp.			
75	room temp.			

} Write 'hotter' if the rice is more than 5°C hotter than the room temperature, or 'room temp'.

Q2 Write down the name of each material. Underneath each one, write the time it took the rice to cool to within 5°C of room temperature.

MATERIAL:				
TIME IN MINUTES:				

Q3 Fill in this bar chart using your results.

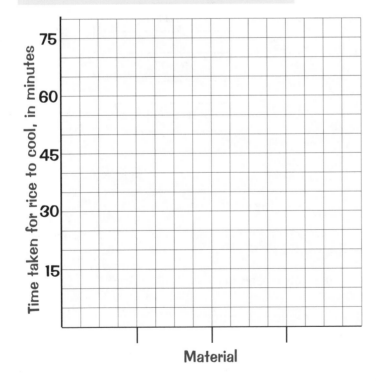

Time taken for rice to cool, in minutes

75
60
45
30
15

Material

The rice took a long time to cool down, but Siegfried's camel didn't mind.

Spare Results:
Foil — 15 mins
Polythene bag — 30 mins
Polystyrene — 60 mins

Bar charts — at number 1 is a bar of gold...

A bar chart is another good way to present your results. You can find out which material was best just with a quick look at the chart. And they make your work look stacks better...

Keeping Things Warm

The wrappings that keep things hot best are the same as the materials that keep things cold best. That's because they're <u>insulators</u>, which stop heat from travelling so well.

Q1   Looking at your results from the last page, fill in the gaps in these sentences.

The .... was best at insulating.

It took .... minutes for the rice to cool.

The .... was worst at insulating.

It took .... minutes for the rice to cool.

The difference between these times is .... minutes.

Insulators' Airport Lounge Strictly No Entry for Heat.

Darn it - I'm in the wrong place!

Insulators make it hard for heat to travel.

Q2   If more than one material kept the rice warm for a long time, what did these materials have in common? Pick out the right words to fill in the gaps in these sentences.

If you only had one good insulator, try to guess what it would have in common with other good insulators.

a) The good insulators were ....

b) The good insulators were ....

c) The good insulators were ....

QUITE THICK	HEAVY
LIGHT	METALS
QUITE THIN	NOT METALS

Q3   Fill in the gaps in these sentences, using the words on the right.

Heat travels easily through .... — they are not

good insulators. Metals get .... and

.... very quickly. Good insulators are not

usually very .... It doesn't matter so much

what .... the insulator is.

hot

colour

cold

metals

heavy

Hunt the insulator — you're getting warmer...

Don't go thinking a saucepan keeps food warm — that's only because it's on a cooker. If it's just standing there, food would get cold in a metal saucepan. Your grub stays hot better in a china dish.

Keeping Things Warm

Here are some more good and bad insulators. Two thin layers of a material provide much better insulation than one thick layer of the same stuff. It's all to do with trapped air... No joke...

Q1 Here's a list of some materials and containers. Tick the ones which you think would be good at insulating and put a cross next to the ones that wouldn't.

a) Polythene bag ....   b) Towel ....   c) Sieve ....

d) Cardboard ....   e) Jumper ....   f) Copper jug ....

Q2 Look at the materials mentioned on page 12 that you <u>didn't</u> choose. Write down which would be good insulators, and which wouldn't.

.... would be good insulators.

.... would not be good insulators.

Q3 I did the experiment again with polystyrene and newspaper, first using one thick layer, and then using two thin layers. I put my results in the bar chart at the bottom of the page. Fill in the gaps in the sentences, using these words.

| one layer | thin layers | air | thin | insulator | layer | between |

It is better to have two .... of good material than

.... of the same thickness. This is because there is

.... between the two layers. Air is a good ....

Having air .... the layers makes the rice keep warm longer.

Two .... layers are often even better than one thick ....

Bar chart: Time taken for rice to cool, in minutes (y-axis: 15, 30, 45, 60, 75, 90, 105). Polystyrene: 1 layer, 2 layers. Newspaper: 1 layer, 2 layers.

I'm getting cold!

??

Eric's metal mountain gear wasn't keeping him warm.

Wrap up warm — put on more layers...

It's all pretty easy really — whatever is good at keeping stuff warm is also good at keeping stuff cold. It's common sense — a thick cup keeps the heat in for a hot drink, or the heat out for a cold drink. It just makes it harder for heat to move at all, in or out. Great stuff.

Good Insulators

So now you know that there are things which are good at keeping things warm and things that are good at keeping things cold. On this page you get to test your knowledge and compare the different types of insulators.

Q1   Look back over the last eight pages on insulators and fill in the following lists.

Polar bears have big white fluffy coats to keep them warm.
List here the four insulators you found best at keeping things hot.

Write a list here of the four insulators you found best at keeping things cold.

....

....

....

....

....

....

....

....

What's black and white and red all over?

I don't know. What is black and white and red all over?

A sunburnt penguin. Ha-ha-ha-haaaa...

Ow!

Polar bears have warm fur — and bad jokes.

Q2   What do these results tell you? Complete the sentences below by circling the right word(s) in the brackets.

The materials which (are / are not) good insulators for hot materials

(are / are not) good insulators for cold materials.

Keep ALL the heat in?— you'd be hot under the collar...

It sounds weird, but the same things that keep things hot keep things cold as well. That means you've only got one load of insulators to learn about, not two. It sounds good to me.

Good Insulators

More interesting stuff about insulating materials. Get your brain cells working and answer a load more questions about keeping things hot or cold.

Vacuum flasks are used to keep liquids hot or cold.
Usually they are used to keep them hot.

Cor Blimey!

Doug was amazed by the big silver shiny thing.

Q1 You are taking a tub of delicious ice cream on a picnic. Some of these materials below could be used to wrap the ice cream to keep it frozen. Write the good insulators on the left, and the bad insulators on the right.

Cling Film   Polystyrene

Thick Foam Sheeting   A Sheet of Tissue Paper

GOOD

Bubble Wrap   Thin Cotton

BAD

ICE CREAM
Strawberry
ICE CREAM

....

....

....

....

Q2 An Eskimo and his igloo have been moved to Africa by a giant hurricane. What should he wrap his igloo in to keep it frozen until he can move it back? Fill in the gap on the right using one of the phrases below.

a sheet of newspaper   metal

palm leaves   some thin cardboard

woollen blankets   a bed sheet

The Eskimo should use

....

to keep his igloo frozen.

Q3 Use the words in the boxes to fill in the gaps in these sentences about winter coats.

hot   insulator   freezing   material   wool   metal   bad   good

An .... would be a good .... to make a winter coat

from. You should use something .... at keeping things

.... or cold, like ....

How's an eskimo mend his roof — I-gloos it together...

There are tons of uses for insulators. Thermos flasks, coats, houses, jumpers, gloves, coffee mugs, diving suits, space suits, food boxes...
The list goes on and on...

Metal, Plastic and Wood

Ed and Liz are stirring hot soup.

Ed is using a wooden spoon, and Liz is using a metal spoon.

After 5 minutes, Ed notices that the handle of his spoon is cool, but Liz's is hot.

That's because heat travels through metal much more easily than it can travel through wood or plastic.

Liz's metal spoon got hot first.

Q1 Use the words from the blue blob to fill in these blanks.

heat

handles

conductors

metal

wood

insulators

.... for hot things like saucepans and irons are often made

of plastic or .... They are not usually made from metal.

The plastic or wood are heat .... — they stop the heat getting

through and burning your hand. Some things are made of metal because you

want the .... to go through easily. That's why a radiator is

made of .... Metals are good heat ....

Q2 Tick the box to show what these things are made of — metal, plastic or wood.

Knife Blade

Metal ☐ Plastic ☐ Wood ☐

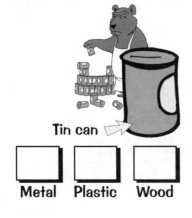

Tin can

Metal ☐ Plastic ☐ Wood ☐

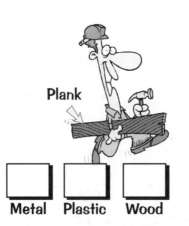

Plank

Metal ☐ Plastic ☐ Wood ☐

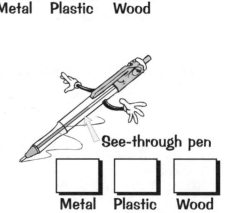

See-through pen

Metal ☐ Plastic ☐ Wood ☐

Oak saucepans — you wooden want that...

So if you <u>want</u> heat to get through, metal is best — you never see wooden radiators. That's why things like saucepans are made of metal — so the heat can get through to the food.

Metal, Plastic and Wood

Sheila wants to make some mini-cauldrons for apprentice witches to use. Help her to choose which materials to make them from. Think about whether you want to use a good heat conductor (to let the heat through), or a bad heat conductor (to stop heat going through).

Q1 Write which material she should <u>NOT</u> use to make the handle. Write a reason why not.

 Pine Wood  Heat-Proof Plastic 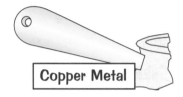 Copper Metal

....

....

Q2 Which material should the base and the main part of the cauldron be made from? Give a reason why that's the best material to use.

 Heat-Proof Plastic  Copper Metal  Pine Wood

The factory made a small mistake with Sheila's mini-cauldron...

....

....

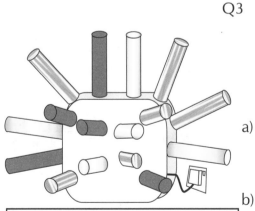

Sheila's Dangerous Spiky Heater

Q3 Sheila's dog has made a heater with rods sticking out of it. The rods are made from metal, heat-proof plastic, and wood. Sheila says it's dangerous — the rods could get hot and burn your fingers if you touched them.

When the heater's been switched on for a while...

a) Which type of rod would be hottest? Write the material.

....

b) Write down one of the types of rod which would heat up less quickly.

....

Copper metal — metal for policemen...

Here's a clue — <u>one</u> material here conducts heat well, and <u>two</u> don't. Think carefully about whether you want the heat to get through or not — and you'll find this a doddle.

Electrical and Heat Conductors

A material which lets electricity go through it is called an <u>electrical conductor</u>. Metals are good electrical conductors.

A material that is a <u>good electrical conductor</u> is probably a <u>good heat conductor</u> too.

A material that is <u>not</u> a good electrical conductor is probably <u>not</u> a good heat conductor.

Q1 Work out if each of the things below is a good heat conductor or a bad heat conductor, and put its name in the right place in the table. Hint: see if it's a good electrical conductor or not.

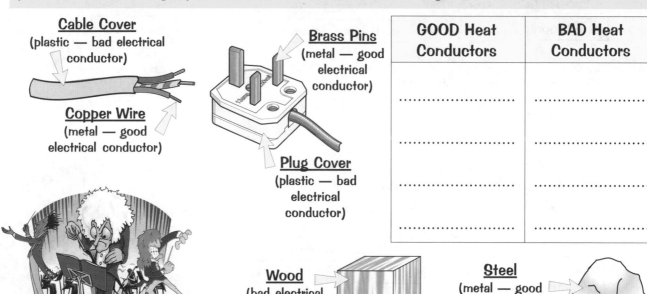

Cable Cover (plastic — bad electrical conductor)

Copper Wire (metal — good electrical conductor)

Brass Pins (metal — good electrical conductor)

Plug Cover (plastic — bad electrical conductor)

GOOD Heat Conductors	BAD Heat Conductors
....	....
....	....
....	....
....	....

<u>Musical</u> conductors have got nothing to do with this page.

Wood (bad electrical conductor)

Steel (metal — good electrical conductor)

Q2 See if each of the things in the pictures below is a good heat conductor or not, then use what you know about electrical conductors to put its name in the right place in the table.

Remember: metals are good electrical conductors.

GOOD Electrical Conductors	BAD Electrical Conductors
....	....
....	....
....	....
....	....

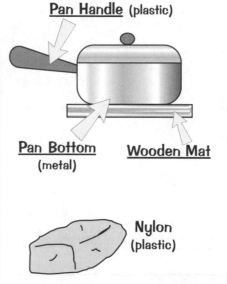

Pan Handle (plastic)

Pan Bottom (metal)

Wooden Mat

Zinc (metal)

Nylon (plastic)

Iron's Handle (plastic)

Iron's Bottom (metal)

Electrical conductors — sparks fly in their buses...

If something conducts heat, chances are it conducts electricity too. That's all there is to it.

Everyday Insulators

You see loads of things every day which are used to keep things hot or keep things cold.

Q1   Here are 5 things that I want to keep <u>warm</u>. Work out which of the 8 things in the box you should use to keep each of them warm, and write the answer underneath.

I've done the first one for you.

a) A house

Double glazed window.

b) A hot water boiler

c) Me when I'm outside

d) A hot drink

e) My dinner

Thick stone wall

Winter jacket

Cotton sunhat

Thick casserole dish

Glass windows

Air gap

Double glazed window

Thick polystyrene walls

Picnic box

Vacuum flask

Foam sheeting

Q2   Here are 4 things that I want to keep <u>cool</u>. Work out which of the 8 things in the box you should use to keep each of them cool, and write the answer underneath.

I've done the first one for you.

a) Me in hot weather

Cotton sunhat.

b) Some sandwiches

c) A cold drink

(This will be the same as one of your answers to Q1.)

d) A house in a hot desert

Chill out — keep it cool...

All the things in the box are good insulators — but you can't use all of them for everything.
Don't go putting your dinner in the winter jacket or yourself in the picnic box. That would be weird.

Keeping Things Cold

There are loads of situations where you might want to keep something cold.

Q1   Tumbo has a problem. He wants to take his monster to school to show his friends, but he has to keep it frozen — if it gets warm it tries to eat people.

He has a plan. He'll try wrapping the monster with a different material each day to see which is the best at keeping the monster cold.

Here are the results of his experiment.

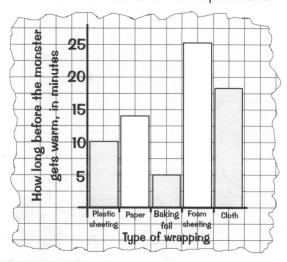

Tumbo has to keep the monster frozen to stop it eating people.

a)   Which material kept the monster cold the longest?

....

b)   Which material was the 2nd best at keeping the monster cold?

....

c)   Why is baking foil not very good at keeping the monster cold?

....

....

Q2   What could Tumbo use to measure the temperature of the monster?

....

Q3   Tumbo wants to keep his milk shake cold too. Which of the materials should he wrap the glass in to keep the milk shake cold the longest?

....

I got a monster cold — I was ill for 6 weeks...

This page should help if you ever have to keep a monster cold. Yes, I know it's not likely, but you never know. If you can remember what things are good insulators, you'll have no problems.

Keeping Things Hot or Cold

Some everyday examples of things that people want to keep hot or cold.
Remember that they need to use some kind of insulator.

Q1   Binsi wants to keep her cocoa warm. Write down three things she could do to help keep it warm.

Hint: she could try wrapping the mug with something. Look back at pages 18 to 22 if you're stuck.

① ....

....

② ....

....

③ ....

....

Binsi wants to keep her cocoa warm.

Q2   Norm doesn't want his giant snowball to melt.
Write down three things he could do to help keep it cold.

He could try wrapping the snowball in something.
Look back at pages 18 to 22 if you're stuck.

① ....

....

② ....

....

③ ....

....

Norm wants to stop his snowball melting.

Don't get into a heated argument about it...

It's all good useful stuff. Now if you build a snowman, you know how to stop it melting so fast.
It might look daft under a pile of old coats, but it'll still be there when everyone else's has melted.

Revision Questions

There are loads of juicy questions squeezed onto these two pages. All the questions here ask about things you've already done in this book, so look back through it if you get stuck.

Q1 Shade in the following thermometers so that they show the temperature written next to them.

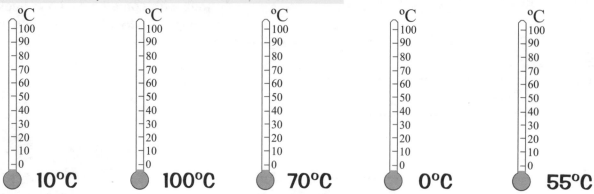

10°C   100°C   70°C   0°C   55°C

Q2 Billy's bowl of milk was 40°C. He left it in the fridge for 15 hours. The inside of the fridge is 5°C. What temperature will his milk be now? (Choose from the numbers in the box.)

40°C / 5°C / 60°C / -5°C

.... °C.

Q3 Name two materials that are good at keeping ice cubes cold and two materials that are bad at keeping ice cubes cold.

Good : .... and ....
Bad : .... and ....

Q4 Some materials are good at keeping ice cubes cold. Are these materials also good at keeping hot things hot? (Circle the right answer.)

Yes   No

Q5 We timed how long it took a choc-ice to melt if we wrapped it in different things. All the results are in the table below.

Fill in the bar chart to show all the information from the table.

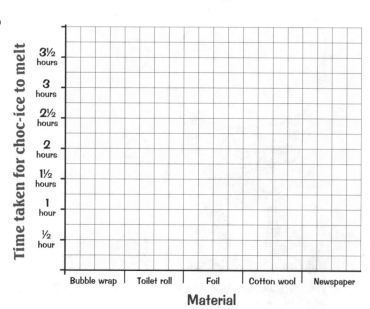

Material	Time in hours
Bubble wrap	3½
Toilet roll	1½
Foil	½
Cotton wool	2½
Newspaper	1½

It's nearly over — keep cool...

Brrr... this page is making me chilly. You can keep cool things _cool_ by putting them in the _fridge_. If you don't have a fridge, you need to _wrap them_ in _insulating stuff_ to stop them warming up.

Revision Questions

Q1 Complete these sentences using the words from the blue blob.

Materials that are good heat conductors are .... conductors of electricity.

Materials that are good heat insulators are .... conductors of electricity.

The handle of the pan is a .... insulator.

The bottom of the pan is a .... conductor.

The handle could be made from .... or ....

The rest of the pan is made of ....

bad good metal good plastic good wood

Q2 There are two sentences below about conductors.
Say whether they are true or false by circling the right answer.

A material that is a good heat conductor is probably a good electrical conductor too. TRUE / FALSE

A material that is not a good heat conductor is probably not a good electrical conductor. TRUE / FALSE

Q3 Circle the things below that are good electrical conductors.

plastic mug   **wooden mug**   **metal mug**

copper wire

Q4 Frank has found an abandoned egg that's still warm. He needs to keep it warm so it will hatch. Write down three things he could do to keep it warm.

① ....

....

② ....

....

③ ....

....

Frankie looks after his egg

... and relax

Things that conduct heat well are completely useless at keeping hot things hot — they just let the heat straight out. All metals conduct heat really well. Wood, plastic and bubblewrap don't.

Index